This copy of

The WOOLLY Jumper JOKE BOOK

BY PETER ELDIN

belongs to

. . . .

Also in Sparrow by Peter Eldin

The Complete Practical Joker
Skool Graffiti
School for Laughs

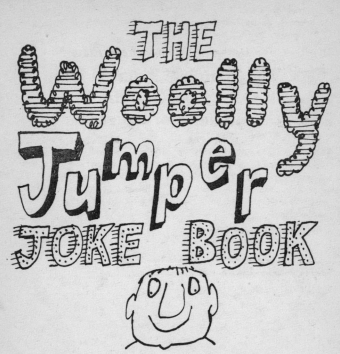

THE Woolly Jumper JOKE BOOK

Peter Eldin

ILLUSTRATED BY Colin West

SPARROW BOOKS

A Sparrow Book
Published by Arrow Books Limited
17-21 Conway Street, London W1P 6JD

An imprint of the Hutchinson Publishing Group

London Melbourne Sydney Auckland
Johannesburg and agencies throughout the world

First published 1984
Reprinted 1984 (twice)
© Eldin Editorial Services 1984
Illustration © Colin West 1984

Set in Linoterm Baskerville by
JH Graphics Ltd, Reading

Printed and bound in Great Britain by
Anchor Brendon Ltd, Tiptree, Essex

ISBN 0 09 935370 9

Contents

WOOLLY JUMPER AND FRIENDS

What do you get if you cross . . .

. . . a kangaroo with a sheep?
A woolly jumper.

. . . a cat with a chemist's shop?
Puss in Boots.

What do you get if you cross . . .

. . . a sheep with six radiators?
Central bleating.

. . . an idiot with a monkey?
A chumpanzee.

. . . a hyena with an Oxo cube?
An animal that makes itself a laughing stock.

. . . a butterfly with a racing driver?
Stirling Moth.

. . . a cow with a camel?
Lumpy milk.

What do you get if you cross . . .

. . . a field of grass with a cow?
A lawn-mooer.

. . . a sheep with a rainstorm?
A wet blanket.

. . . a tulip with a camel?
A flower than can last for days without water.

. . . a frog with a chair?
A toadstool.

What do you get if you cross . . .

. . . a snake with a magic spell?
Abradacobra.

. . . a herd of cows with a panic situation?
Udder chaos.

. . . complete quiet with a dog?
Hush puppies.

. . . a panda with a harmonium?
Pandamonium.

. . . a cow with a rich Arab?
A milk sheikh.

What do you get if you cross . . .

. . . a crocodile with a flower?
I don't know – but don't try smelling it!

. . . a baby's bed with a sheep?
Cotton wool.

. . . an adder with a trombone?
A snake in the brass.

What do you get if you cross . . .

. . . a horse with a football player?
A centaur-forward.

. . . a furry animal with a mint?
A Polo bear.

. . . a worm with a cornfield?
Something that goes in one ear and out another.

. . . a centipede with a parrot?
A walkie-talkie.

What do you get if you cross . . .

. . . a cow with someone who lives in the Arctic?
An eskimoo.

. . . a galaxy and a toad?
Star warts.

. . . a kangaroo with a calendar?
A leap year.

. . . a butterfly with a Russian Naval
Commander?
A Red Admiral.

What do you get if you cross . . .

. . . a cat with a Chinese leader?
Miaow Tse Tung.

. . . a flea with a Scotsman?
Hop-scotch.

. . . a horse with a television aerial?
A reindeer.

. . . a crocodile with an angry dog?
Very nervous postmen!

. . . a sheep with a submarine?
A ewe-boat.

. . . a flea with a cheerful person?
A hoptomist.

What do you get if you cross . . .

. . . an elk with a cocoa bean?
A chocolate mousse.

. . . a horse with a skunk?
Whinny the Pooh.

. . . a cat with a Chinese city?
A Peking Tom.

. . . a glow-worm with a python?
A twenty-foot strip-light.

. . . a cat with a lemon?
A sourpuss.

What do you get if you cross . . .

. . . a snake with a Lego set?
A boa constructor.

. . . some small rodents with breakfast cereal?
Mice Krispies.

. . . an arithmetic teacher with a crocodile?
Snappy answers.

. . . a cat with a ball of wool?
Mittens.

What do you get if you cross . . .

. . . an Irishman with a spider?
A Paddy longlegs.

. . . a frog with a can of drink?
Croaka Cola.

. . . a space pistol with a cheer and a
hippopotamus?
A hip-hippo-ray gun!

. . . a walker with a flea?
An itch-hiker.

What do you get if you cross . . .

. . . a hippopotamus with someone who always feels ill?
A hippochondriac.

. . . a frog with a flower?
A croakus.

. . . a flea with a rabbit?
Bugs Bunny.

. . . a kitten with part of a sawn tree?
A cat-a-logue.

. . . a cat with a periodical?
A mewspaper.

. . . a frog with a knife and a spy?
A croak and dagger agent.

What do you get if you cross . . .

. . . a prehistoric monster with a sleeping person?
A dinasnore.

. . . a cow with a mule?
Milk with a kick in it.

What do you get if you cross . . .

. . . a policeman with a cow?
Truncheon meat.

. . . music with an insect?
A humbug.

. . . a tin of plasters with a cat?
A first aid kit.

. . . a cowardly cow with a pullover?
A yellow jersey.

What do you get if you cross . . .

. . . a cow with an American city?
Moo York.

What do you get if you cross . . .

. . . a bout of hiccups with a cow?
A cow that churns its own butter.

. . . a pub with a line of bees?
A barbecue (bar-bee-queue).

. . . a whale with a nun?
Blubber and sister.

What do you get if you cross . . .

. . . a rabbit with a leek?
A bunion.

. . . a baby goat with an anagram?
A crazy mixed-up kid.

. . . a dog with a giraffe?
An animal that barks at low flying aircraft.

. . . a giraffe with a hedgehog?
A twenty-foot toothbrush.

. . . a snake with a mathematician?
An adder.

What do you get if you cross . . .

. . . an ant with a block of ice?
Antifreeze.

. . . an insect with a famous stunt man?
Weevil Knieval.

. . . a cow with a pile of money?
Rich milk.

. . . a frog with a sweet?
A lollihop.

. . . a cow with a printing press?
A moospaper.

What do you get if you cross . . .

. . . a canine with a fire?
A hot dog.

. . . a bottle of medicine with a horse?
Cough stirrup.

. . . a toad with a hooter?
A frog-horn.

What do you get if you cross . . .

. . . a snake with a government employee?
A civil serpent.

. . . a dog with an arrow?
A pointer.

. . . some luminous paint with a worm?
A glow-worm.

. . . a cat with a coin?
Money in the kitty.

. . . a sheepdog with a bunch of daisies?
Collie-flowers.

. . . a cow with a surgeon?
Cow-operation.

. . . a cow with a sheep and a baby goat?
The Milky Baa Kid.

CROSSED LINES

What do you get if you cross . . .

. . . an English king with a fireplace?
Alfred the Grate.

. . . eighteen gallons of beer with a harmonica?
A barrel organ.

. . . an Italian with a Scottish mist?
Roman in the gloamin'!

What do you get if you cross . . .

. . . a burglar with an orchestra?
Robbery with violins.

. . . a policeman with a ghost?
An inspectre.

What do you get if you cross . . .

. . . a Scottish legend with a singer?
The Loch Ness Songster.

. . . an elf with the Paris underground?
A metrognome.

. . . William with a power station?
An electricity bill.

. . . petrol with an insult?
Crude oil.

. . . a Scottish farmer with a beautiful day?
McKay while the sun shines!

. . . a skeleton with a famous detective?
Sherlock Bones.

. . . a numbskull with a flower?
A blooming idiot.

What do you get if you cross . . .

. . . a musical instrument with an Ancient
Briton?
An Anglo Saxophone.

. . . a successful book with a perfume?
A best smeller.

. . . a bed with a spy?
An undercover agent.

What do you get if you cross . . .

. . . a pool of water with a spy?
James Pond.

. . . an ear of corn and a bicycle pump?
Puffed wheat.

. . . a spy with a spy?
A double agent.

. . . a dentist with a manicurist?
A couple that fight tooth and nail.

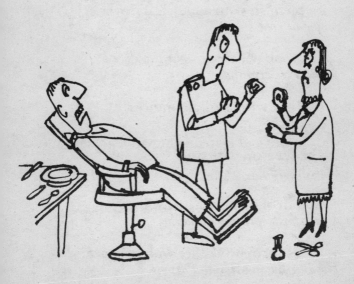

What do you get if you cross . . .

. . . a blemish with a four-leaf clover?
A spot of good luck.

. . . a crook with a cement mixer?
A hardened criminal.

. . . an axe with a small branch?
A chopstick.

. . . heavy rain with an electric bulb?
Floodlighting.

. . . a dab of glue with an aspirin?
A cure for a splitting headache.

. . . a lost property office with two vicars?
The Bureau of Missing Parsons.

What do you get if you cross . . .

. . . a famous composer with an Indian?
Haydn Sikh.

. . . an English king with a fraction?
Henry the 1/8th.

. . . an oil slick with a stone?
Blackpool rock.

. . . an ice-cream manufacturer with an eastern city?
The Walls of Jericho.

. . . a party with a campsite?
Intense excitement!

. . . three wings with three legs and two beaks?
A bird with spare parts.

What do you get if you cross . . .

. . . an ancient Egyptian with a door bell?
Toot-and-come-in.

. . . a common illness with a spy?
A code in the nose.

. . . a £5 note with a refrigerator?
Iced lolly.

. . . a group of undertakers with Wembley
Exhibition Hall?
The Hearse of the Year Show.

What do you get if you cross . . .

. . . a Viking with a secret message?
Norse code.

. . . a library with a karate expert?
A book chop.

. . . an ancient British king with a chiropodist?
William the corn-curer.

. . . a skeleton with a clock?
A rattling good time.

. . . a judge with a tailor?
A law suit.

What do you get if you cross . . .

. . . a road with a load of diamonds?
Mugged.

. . . a load of diamonds with a road?
A jewel carriageway.

. . . something chewy with a pair of wellingtons?
Gumboots.

. . . a group of stars with a silver cup?
A constellation prize.

What do you get if you cross . . .

. . . the moon with the top of a house?
A lunatic.

. . . a shopping centre with gold paint?
A gilt complex.

. . . a hill with an infant school?
A nursery slope.

. . . an elf with a boat travelling from Dover to Calais?
A cross-channel fairy.

What do you get if you cross . . .

. . . a river with a piano?
The Water Music.

. . . a street with an army officer?
Major road ahead.

What do you get if you cross . . .

. . . a stomach with an x-ray?
Bellyvision.

. . . a sailor with a torch?
A salt and battery.

. . . a chimney with an illness?
A touch of the flue.

. . . a gardener with a magazine?
Weeder's Digest.

What do you get if you cross . . .

. . . a writing desk with ten people who are lost?
The bureau of missing persons.

. . . a carpenter, Terry Wogan, and a television show?
'Plankety Plank'.

. . . a telephone with a flannel?
Something that is ringing wet.

. . . a wedding with a lighthouse?
A marriage that is on the rocks.

What do you get if you cross . . .

. . . a dance with a tin-opener?
The Can-Can.

. . . an office with people who study legends?
The Bureau of Mything Persons.

. . . someone from Iceland with someone from Cuba?
An ice cube.

. . . a bout of madness with a bunch of fleas?
Loony ticks.

. . . spacemen with lots of X's?
Astronauts and crosses.

. . . a TV with a TV?
A television repeat.

What do you get if you cross . . .

. . . your mother's sister with a refrigerator?
Auntifreeze.

. . . Father Christmas with the clapping of hands?
Santaplause.

. . . a piece of paper with two famous composers?
A Chopin Liszt.

. . . Santa Claus with a tug of war team?
Christmas 'eave!

. . . a hiker with a gossip?
A walkie-talkie.

JESTER JOKE

What do you get if you cross . . .

. . . a midget Indian with a joker?
Minihaha.

. . . a joker with a fraction?
A half-wit.

. . . a magazine with a Welshman and a joker?
Reader's Dai-jest.

. . . a joke with a professor?
A wisecrack

What do you get if you cross . . .

. . . a plot of land with a joker?
A field of corn.

. . . a joker with British Rail?
Inter-witty.

. . . a joker with a chicken?
A comedihen.

. . . an angler with a joker?
Fish and quips.

. . . a banana with a joker?
Peels of laughter.

What do you get if you cross . . .

. . . a marauding leader with a corny joker?
Attila the Pun.

. . . a joke with a boy puppet?
Punocchio.

. . . a joker with a meal?
A feast of fun.

. . . a joker with a ball of wool?
A knit-wit.

What do you get if you cross . . .

. . . a drill with a joker?
A boring joke.

. . . a clock with a joker?
A laugh a minute.

What do you get if you cross . . .

. . . a boxer with a joker?
Punchlines.

. . . some geese with a joker?
A gaggle of giggles.

. . . a joker with a pile of knickers?
A jester drawers.

. . . a joker with a mad strangler?
A joker choker.

What do you get if you cross . . .

. . . a joker with an American gangster?
Riddled with bullets.

. . . an escapologist with a joker?
Bound and gagged.

. . . a monkey with a Scottish dance and a joker?
An ape-reel fool.

CHOP CHOP!

What do you get if you cross . . .

. . . a pig with an elephant?
Large pork chops.

. . . a pig with a zebra?
Striped sausages.

. . . an elephant with peanut butter?
An elephant that sticks to the roof of your mouth.

. . . a pig with a naked athlete?
Streaky bacon.

What do you get if you cross . . .

. . . an elephant with a jar of jam?
A jam sandwich that never forgets.

. . . a pig with a horse?
A neigh-boar.

. . . a pig with a writing implement?
Pen and oink.

. . . an elephant with a goldfish?
Swimming trunks.

What do you get if you cross . . .

. . . an elephant with a mouse?
Large holes in the skirting-board.

. . . an elephant with a telephone?
A trunk call.

. . . a pig with some medicine?
Oinkment.

. . . a pig with a bad actor?
A big ham.

What do you get if you cross . . .

. . . an elephant with a hosepipe?
A jumbo jet.

. . . a pig with a drummer?
Ham rolls.

. . . a pig with a laundry?
Hogwash.

. . . an elephant with a packet of sedatives?
Trunkquillizers.

. . . a pig with a thief?
A humburglar.

. . . an elephant with nonsense?
Mumbo jumbo.

What do you get if you cross . . .

. . . a pig with a hospital vehicle?
A hambulance.

. . . a pig with the M1?
A road hog.

. . . the M1 with a pig?
Run over.

. . . an elephant with a boy scout?
An elephant that helps old ladies cross the road.

What do you get if you cross . . .

. . . a tipsy elephant with a motorist?
A trunk an' driver.

. . . a pig with a mathematician?
A pork pi.

. . . a pig with a small tree?
An 'ambush.

. . . a pig with a story?
A pig-tale.

FOOD, GLORIOUS FOOD

What do you get if you cross . . .

. . . food with a pair of roller skates?
Meals on wheels.

What do you get if you cross . . .

. . . a potato with a sponge?
A vegetable that soaks up the gravy.

. . . a raisin with a power station?
An electric currant.

. . . a tomato with an insult?
Tomato sauce.

. . . a tomato with a banana skin?
A pair of red slippers.

. . . a loaf with a golfer?
Bread and putter.

What do you get if you cross . . .

. . . a fruit with a Welshman?
A taffy apple.

. . . a jelly with a tall structure in Paris?
The Trifle Tower.

. . . a plum with an accident?
A damson in distress.

. . . a white cake with a monkey?
A meringue-outang.

. . . a pile of bricks with a crate of whisky?
A wall that is plastered.

What do you get if you cross . . .

. . . a pound of apples with a pair of boxing gloves?
Cider punch.

. . . a jelly with a broken-down boat?
A nervous wreck.

. . . a yellow fruit with a Greek singer?
Banana Mouskouri.

. . . a dog with a jelly?
The collie wobbles.

What do you get if you cross . . .

. . . a cloud with a barrel of beer?
An alestorm.

. . . a highwayman with a pickle?
Dirk Gherkin.

. . . a radish with a fire bell?
A repeater alarm.

. . . an athlete with a vegetable?
A runner bean.

. . . a piece of meat with a union representative?
A chop steward.

. . . some pasta with a cowboy film?
A spaghetti western.

What do you get if you cross . . .

. . . some pasta with a motorway?
Spaghetti junction.

. . . a spaceman with an almond?
An astronut.

. . . a diamond with a cabbage and a weighing machine?
A jewel cabbage-weigh.

What do you get if you cross . . .

. . . a piece of toast with an egg and an eiderdown?
Breakfast in bed.

. . . an aeroplane with an apple tart?
Pie in the sky.

. . . a house with a quarter pound of chopped meat?
A homeburger.

. . . a bee with a quarter pound of chopped meat?
A humburger.

What do you get if you cross . . .

. . . a church choir with a quarter pound of chopped meat?
A hymnburger.

. . . a hammer with a biscuit?
Crumbs.

. . . chocolate with a madman?
A coconut.

. . . a piece of meat with a Kung Fu expert?
A karate chop.

. . . a Kung Fu expert with a vegetable?
Bruce Pea.

What do you get if you cross . . .

. . . elves with some pastry?
Fairy cakes.

. . . the Lord of the Jungle with almond paste?
Tarzipan.

. . . a Scotsman with a yellow dessert?
Tartan custard.

. . . a football team with ice-cream?
Aston Vanilla.

What do you get if you cross . . .

. . . a sandwich with a Parisian cathedral?
The lunchpack of Notre Dame.

. . . an alcoholic drink with a hairdresser?
A rum baba.

. . . a monster with a bowl of soup?
Scream of tomato.

BIRDS OF A FEATHER

What do you get if you cross . . .

. . . a woodpecker with a carrier pigeon?
A bird that knocks before it delivers a message.

What do you get if you cross . . .

. . . a greedy cat with a roast duck?
A duck-filled-fattypuss.

. . . a lady's wig with a duck and a cat?
A plait-filled-duckypuss.

. . . a hen with a monkey?
A swinging chick.

. . . a hen with a banjo?
A chicken that plucks itself.

What do you get if you cross . . .

. . . a chicken with a parrot?
Fowl language.

. . . a duck with a breakfast cereal?
Quacker Oats.

. . . something of mine with a blackbird and a
piece of fried potato?
A my-crow chip.

. . . a bird with a skunk?
Something that stinks to high heaven.

What do you get if you cross . . .

. . . a skunk with an owl?
A bird that smells but doesn't give a hoot.

. . . a bottle of milk with a duck?
Cream Quackers.

. . . a pigeon with a frog and a prehistoric animal?
A pigeon-toad dinosaur.

. . . an owl with an oyster?
A creature that drops pearls of wisdom.

What do you get if you cross . . .

. . . a budgie with a lawn mower?
Shredded tweet.

. . . a parrot with a gorilla?
I don't know – but if he says 'Pretty Polly' smile!

. . . a duck with a fire?
A firequacker.

What do you get if you cross . . .

. . . a watch with a parrot?
Politicks.

. . . a duck with a television show?
Quackerjack.

. . . a dove with a dictionary?
Pigeon English.

What do you get if you cross . . .

. . . a chicken with a centipede?
A chicken from which everyone can have a leg.

. . . a vampire with a duck?
Count Duckula.

. . . a chicken with a cross-country motorcyclist?
Scrambled eggs.

. . . a parrot with a rifle?
A parrot-trooper.

. . . a penguin with a sheep?
A sheepskin dinner-jacket.

What do you get if you cross . . .

. . . a blackbird with an idiot?
A raven lunatic!

. . . several ducks with a crate?
A box of quackers.

. . . a hen with some gunpowder?
An eggsplosion.

. . . a chicken with a glass of whisky?
Scotch eggs.

What do you get if you cross . . .

. . . a homing pigeon with a parrot?
A bird that can ask the way if it gets lost.

. . . a chicken with a torch?
A battery hen.

. . . a duck with a monster?
Count Quackula.

. . . a chicken with a cement mixer?
A bricklayer.

What do you get if you cross . . .

. . . a meal with a scavenging bird?
A luncheon vulture.

. . . a bird with a coal pit?
A mynah bird.

. . . a hen with an electric organ?
Hammond eggs.

What do you get if you cross . . .

. . . a coal pit with a zero and a parrot?
Mine-o-poly.

. . . a chicken with a television?
Hentertainment!

. . . a bird with a magician?
A flying sorcerer.

What do you get if you cross . . .

. . . a single sound with a parrot?
Monopoly.

. . . a chicken with a kangaroo?
Pouched eggs.

. . . a hen with a waiter?
A bird that lays tables.

. . . a hen with a tongue and a hand?
Finger-lickin' chicken.

SOUNDS FISHY

What do you get if you cross . . .

. . . a haddock with a glove?
Fish fingers.

What do you get if you cross . . .

. . . a Russian leader with the head of a college?
A tsar-dean.

. . . a guitarist with a fish?
Julian Bream.

. . . a light bulb with a fish?
An electric shark.

What do you get if you cross . . .

. . . a killer shark with an old-time comedian?
Jaws Formby.

. . . a leader of the Mafia with a fish?
The Codfather.

. . . a Scottish lake with a man-eating shark?
Loch Jaw.

. . . a crook with a crustacean?
A smash and crab raid.

What do you get if you cross . . .

. . . a whale with some scales and a train depot?
A whale-weigh station.

. . . a television performer with a haddock?
A starfish.

. . . a fish with a motor cycle?
A motor-pike.

. . . an American president with a killer shark?
Jaws Washington.

What do you get if you cross . . .

. . . a fish with a murderer?
Jack the Kipper.

. . . a telegraphic communication with a fish?
Morse cod.

. . . a madman with an octopus?
A crazy, mixed-up squid.

. . . a fish with a musical instrument?
A piano tuna.

What do you get if you cross . . .

. . . a school of fish with a posh car?
Shoals Royce.

. . . eight arms with a watch?
A clocktopus.

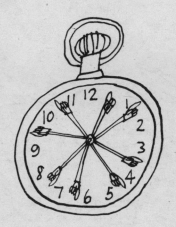

. . . an American outlaw with a fish?
Billy the Cod.

. . . an American outlaw with an undersea
creature?
Billy the Squid.

. . . a fisherman with a musical instrument?
A castanet.

TRANSPORTS OF DELIGHT

What do you get if you cross...

... a class of brainy children with an
underground train?
A tube of Smarties.

... British Rail with a brain?
A train of thought.

What do you get if you cross . . .

. . . an aeroplane with a dog?
A Skye terrier.

. . . an aeroplane with a magician?
A flying sorcerer.

. . . a giant gorilla with a jet aeroplane?
King Kongcorde.

. . . a motor car with a book?
An autobiography.

What do you get if you cross . . .

. . . a fast car with a stiff joint?
Vroomatism!

. . . a jeep with a sheep dog?
A landrover.

. . . a river with a boat?
To the other side.

. . . the Atlantic with the 'Titanic'?
Halfway.

What do you get if you cross . . .

. . . a stomach with an aeroplane?
A bellycopter.

. . . run-down Volkswagens with a house?
An old Volks home.

. . . a round black hat with a jet engine?
A fast bowler.

. . . lots of motor cars with lots of strawberries?
A traffic jam.

MORE CROSSED LINES

What do you get if you cross . . .

. . . a terrorising invader with a cake?
Attila the Bun.

. . . a plate with a telephone?
A crock-a-dial.

What do you get if you cross . . .

. . . some bubblebath with a famous detective?
Sherlock Foams.

. . . a side-street with a hairdresser?
Alley Barber.

What do you get if you cross . . .

. . . a guitar with a lamp?
Light music.

. . . a planet with a public house?
A Mars bar.

. . . a Welshman with an alternative route?
A Daiversion.

. . . a wandering elf with someone crazy?
A gnomad.

What do you get if you cross . . .

. . . an illness with karate?
Kung Flu.

. . . a young child with an Indian guitar?
A baby-sitar.

. . . a burglar with Disneyland?
Someone who takes the Mickey.

. . . black and white stripes with red spots?
A zebra with measles.

What do you get if you cross . . .

. . . a beach with a wicked old lady?
A sandwitch.

. . . a song with an Eskimo?
Freeze a jolly good fellow!

. . . a conjurer with a writer?
A magic spell.

What do you get if you cross . . .

. . . five toes with a cry and something to keep you cool?
A footbawl fan.

. . . a cricket bat with a whistle?
A willow warbler.

. . . a vine with a pile of bricks and some crockery?
The Grape Wall of China.

. . . someone from France with someone from Poland?
A French polisher.

. . . an Egyptian mummy with a swot?
Someone who is wrapped up in his work.

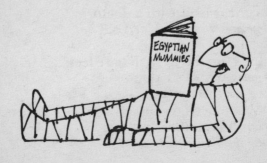

What do you get if you cross . . .

. . . someone who is broke with a cowboy film star?
Skint Eastwood.

. . . a citrus fruit with a doctor?
Lemon-aid.

. . . the Himalayas with bare feet?
Sore soles.

. . . someone who eats spinach with someone who makes clothes?
Popeye the Tailorman.

What do you get if you cross . . .

. . . a tin with someone who is happy?
American (A-merry-can).

. . . a hairless man with a soap-powder?
Bald automatic.

. . . a lamp with a lot of questions?
A 100 what bulb.

. . . an ocean with a thief?
A crime wave.

. . . an escapologist with an employee?
Someone who gets tied up at work.

. . . a watch with a crazy person?
A cuckoo clock.

. . . a boy puppet with a top?
Spinocchio.

What do you get if you cross . . .

. . . a telephone with two vicars?
A parson to parson call.

. . . a newspaper editor with a cannibal chief?
An editor-in-chief.

. . . a friend with a calculator?
A friend you can count on.

What do you get if you cross . . .

. . . a monster with Father Christmas?
Santa Claws.

. . . a monster with a telescope?
A horrorscope.

. . . electric blankets with toasters?
People who pop out of bed in the morning.

. . . a skeleton with a French emperor?
Napoleon Boneypart.

. . . double glazing with 'Star Wars'?
Draught Evader.

. . . an athlete with a beach?
Quicksand.

. . . a dentist with a judge?
The tooth, the whole tooth, and nothing but the tooth.